SELECTIONS FOR SATB CHORUS

GARETH MA...

VOICES

Novello Publishing Limited
part of The Music Sales Group
London / New York / Paris / Sydney / Copenhagen / Berlin / Madrid / Hong Kong / Tokyo

PUBLISHED BY

NOVELLO PUBLISHING LIMITED
PART OF THE MUSIC SALES GROUP
14-15 BERNERS STREET, LONDON W1T 3LJ, UK.

EXCLUSIVE DISTRIBUTORS:

MUSIC SALES LIMITED
DISTRIBUTION CENTRE, NEWMARKET ROAD,
BURY ST EDMUNDS, SUFFOLK IP33 3YB, UK.

MUSIC SALES PTY LIMITED
UNITS 3-4, 17 WILLFOX STREET, CONDELL PARK
NSW 2200, AUSTRALIA.

ORDER NO. NOV164439
ISBN 978-1-78305-411-4

EDITED BY JONATHAN WIKELEY.
MUSIC PROCESSED BY PAUL EWERS MUSIC DESIGN.

WITH THANKS TO
MICHAEL HIGGINS, ALEXANDRA JOHNSON,
KARYN HUGHES AND GARETH MALONE.

PRINTED IN THE EU.

VOICES IS A COLLECTION

OF MY FAVOURITE SONGS -

SOME CONTEMPORARY,

SOME MORE TRADITIONAL

BUT ALL NEWLY ARRANGED

TO CREATE A COMPLETELY FRESH,

CHORAL SOUND.

I HOPE YOU ENJOY SINGING

THEM AS MUCH AS

WE ENJOYED RECORDING THEM.

Hamburg Song

Words & Music by Richard Hughes, James Sanger, Tim Rice-Oxley
& Tom Chaplin, arr. Geoff Lawson

give much more than I'd ev - er ask for.

give_ much more_ than I'd ev - er ask_ for.

give much more than I'd ev - er ask for.

give much more than I'd ev - er ask for.

Will____ you see__ me in the end,____ or is it just a

Will____ you see__ me in the end, or a

Will____ you see__ me in the end, or____ a

Will you see__ me in the end,

6

Try Sleeping with a Broken Heart

Words & Music by Alicia Keys, Jeff Bhasker & Patrick Reynolds,
arr. Michael Higgins & Gareth Malone

20

28

bed,   lone - ly,   own me,   no-bo-dy ev-er shut it down_ like_

bed,   lone - ly,   own me,   ev-er shut it down_ like_

Sleep-ing with a bro - ken heart?_   Bro-ken heart?_

Sleep-ing with a bro - ken heart?_   Bro-ken heart?_

Sleep-ing with a bro - ken heart?_   Bro-ken heart?_

bed,   lone - ly,   own me,   ev-er shut it down_ like_

___ Sleep-ing with a bro-ken heart?_____   Bro - ken heart?_

___ Sleep-ing with a bro-ken heart?_____   Bro - ken heart?_

___ Sleep-ing with a bro-ken heart?_____   Bro - ken heart?_

70

I'm gon-na hold_ on_ to the times_ that_ we had_ to-night._

I'm gon-na hold_ on to the times_ that_ we had_ to - night._

I'm gon-na hold_ on to the times_ that_ we had_ to - night._

I'm gon-na hold_ on to the times_ that_ we had_ to - night._

ah_

ah_

ah_

ah_

Now sleeps the crimson petal

Words by Alfred Tennyson, Music by Paul Mealor

* This may be sung by second sops only, or, the altos may be divided here instead.

42

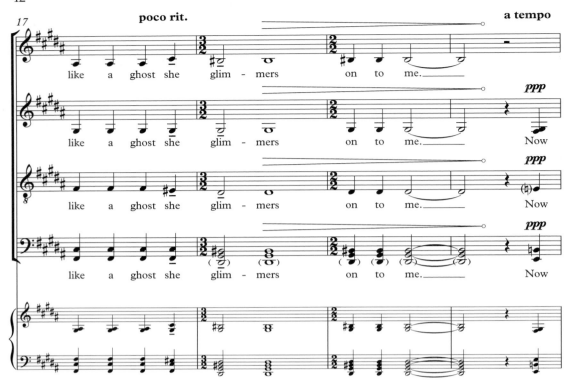

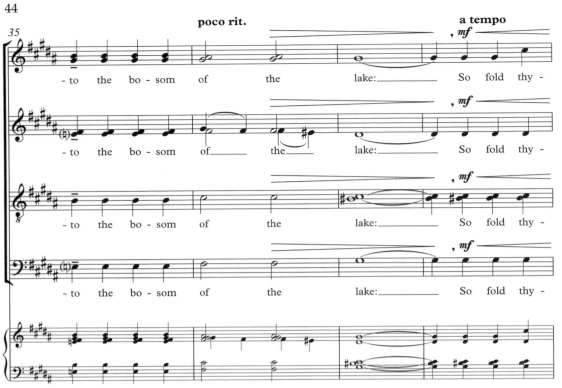

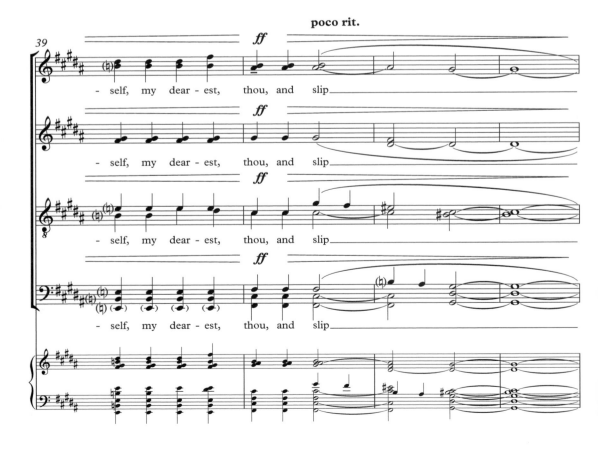

* This may be sung by second sops only, or, the altos may be divided here instead.

Calgary

Words & Music by Justin Vernon & Matt McCaughan,
arr. Fyfe Dangerfield

Choir 1 should stand on the right of the stage, Choir 2 on the left.

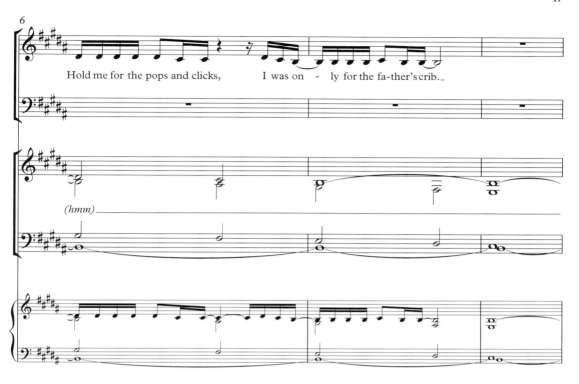

Hold me for the pops and clicks, I was on - ly for the fa-ther's crib.

(hmm)

Hair, old, long, a - long, Your

(hmm)

neck on to your shoul - der blades, ah

(hmm)

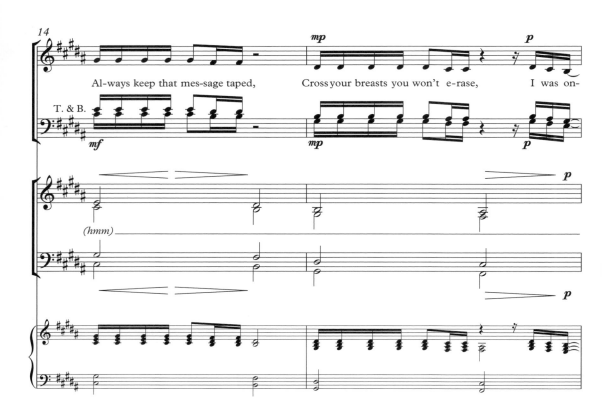

Al - ways keep that mes - sage taped, Cross your breasts you won't e - rase, I was on-

(hmm)

- ly for your ve - ry space.

(hmm)

Hip, un - der noth - ing, Propped up by your oth-er one,

Hip, un - der noth - ing, Propped up by your oth - er one, Face a-

know that all the rope's in-side,___ I was on - ly for to die be-side.___

hmm

know that all the rope's in-side,___ I was on - ly for to die be-side.___

hmm

Sold, I'm ev - er, hmm___

hmm___

hmm___ Op-en ears and op-en eyes, hmm___

TENOR

54

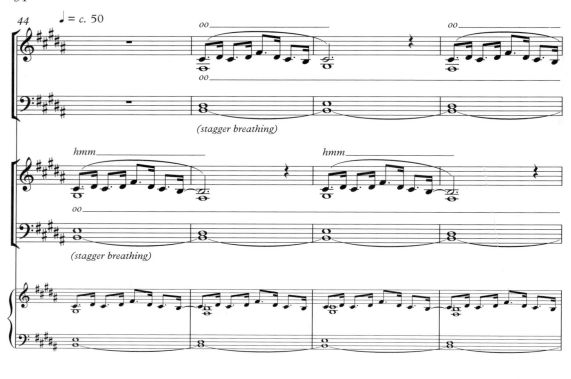

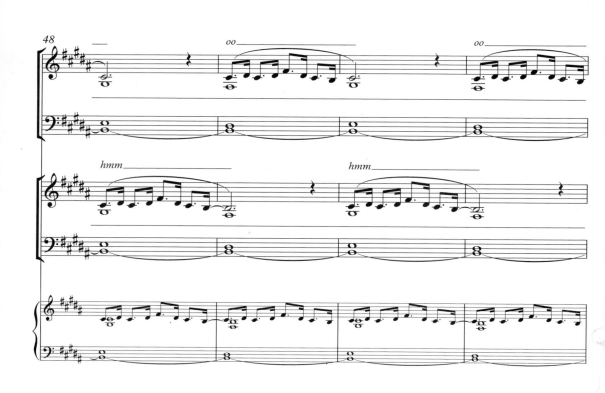

Nights in White Satin

Words & Music by Justin Hayward,
arr. Gareth Malone

White Winter Hymnal

Words & Music by Robin Pecknold,
arr. Michael Higgins

18

21

39

102

No Surprises

Words & Music by Thomas Yorke, Jonathan Greenwood,
Colin Greenwood, Edward O'Brien & Philip Selway,
arr. Gareth Malone

110

112

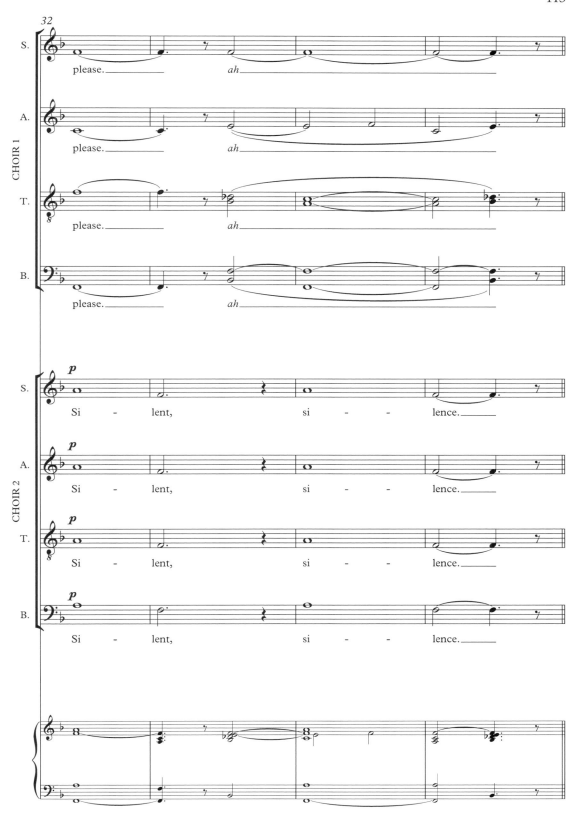

This is my fi-nal fit,___ my fi-nal bel-ly ache.

This is my fi-nal fit,___ my fi-nal bel-ly ache.

This is my fi-nal fit,___ my fi-nal bel-ly ache.

This is my fi-nal fit,___ my fi-nal bel-ly ache.

ah___

ah___

ah___

ah___

ah___

ah___

ah___

ah___

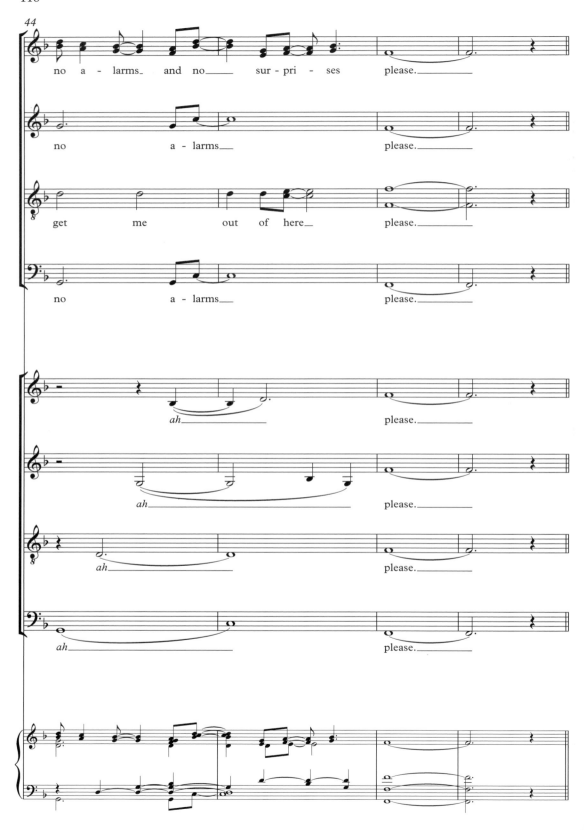

121

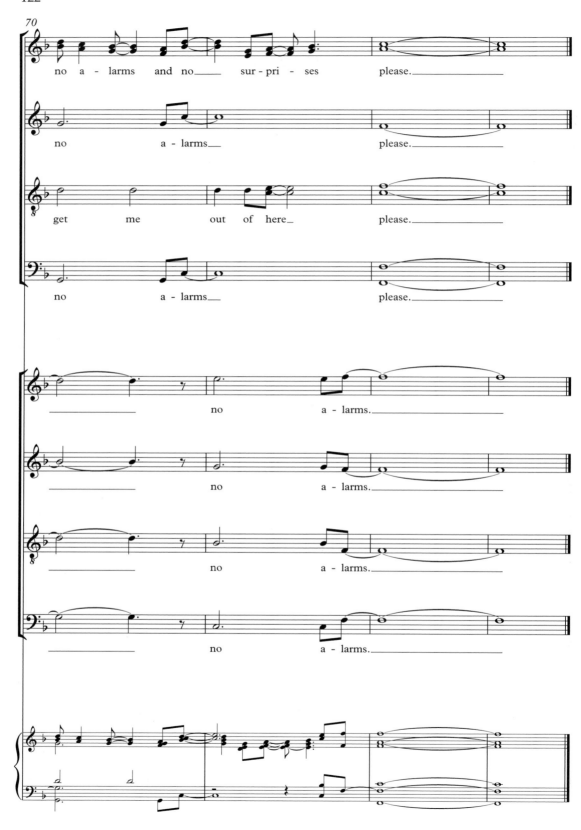

Video Games

Words & Music by Elizabeth Grant & Justin Parker,
arr. Gareth Malone

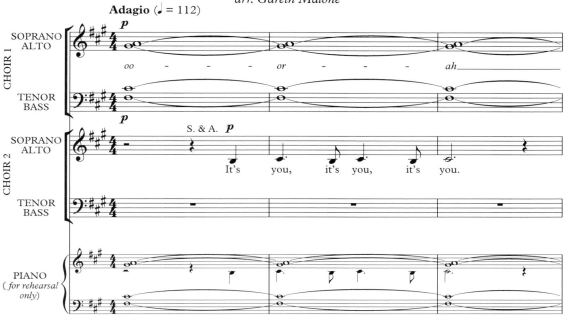

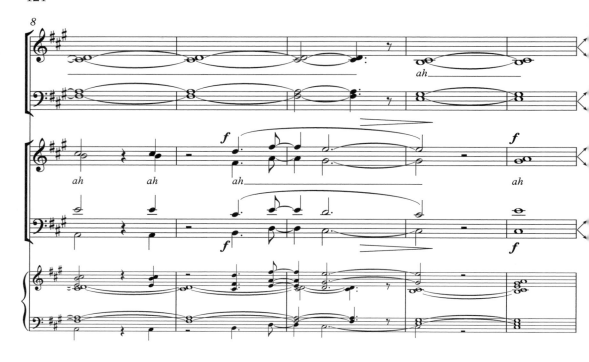

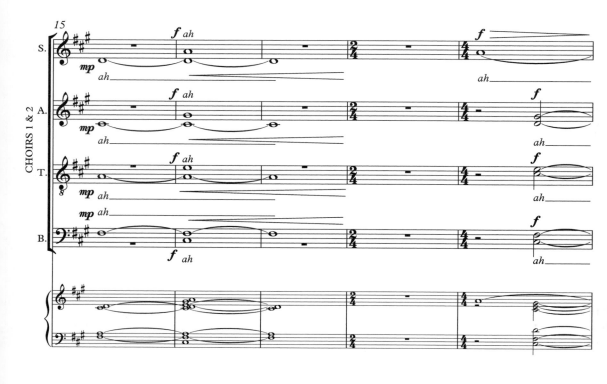

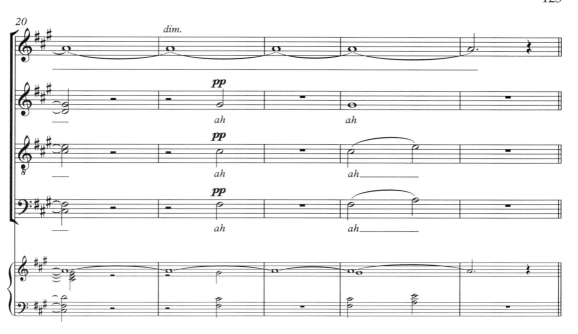

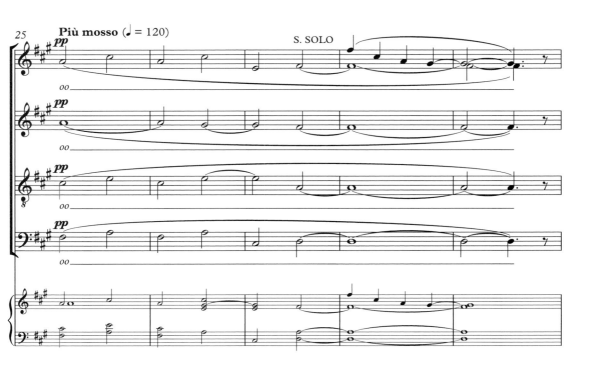

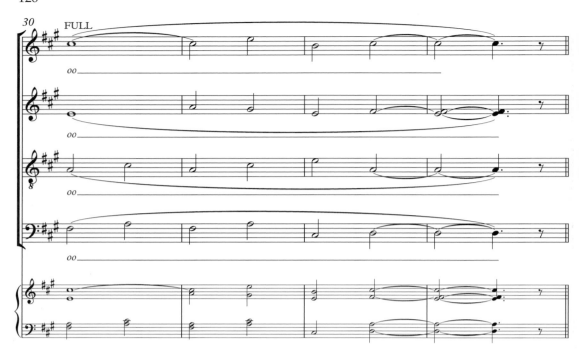

130

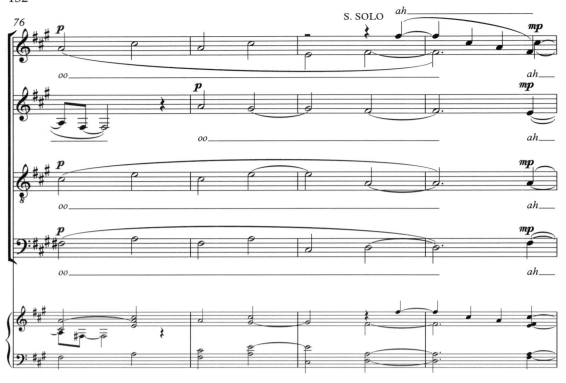

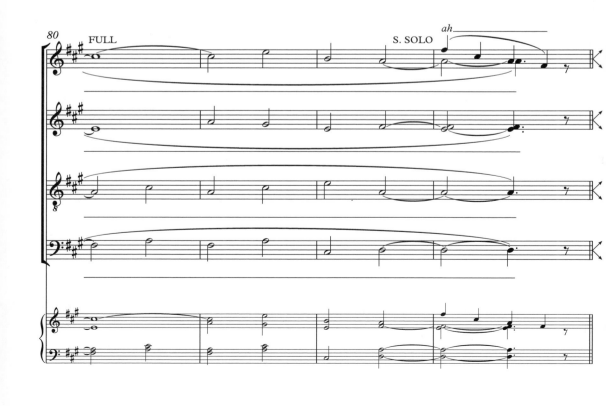

134

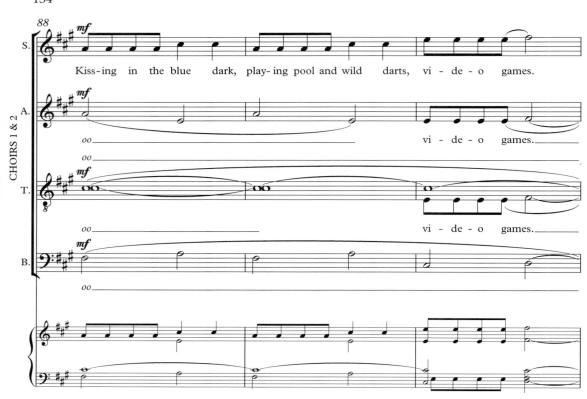

136

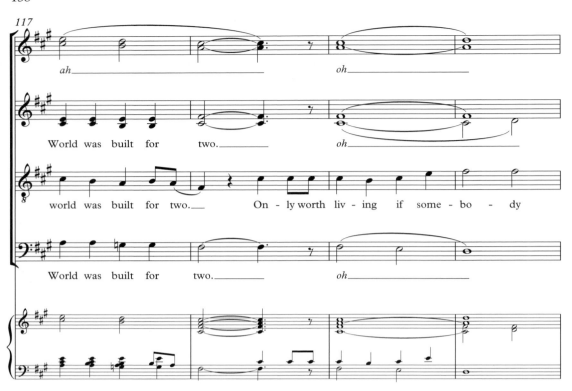

117

ah_____ oh_____

World was built for two.____ oh_____

world was built for two.___ On - ly worth liv - ing if some - bo - dy

World was built for two._____ oh_____

121

Is lov - ing you,____ and ba - by, now you do._____

is lov - ing you.____

I Can't Make You Love Me

Words & Music by Mike Reid & Allen Shamblin,
arr. Rupert Christie

140

142

Go Your Own Way

Words & Music By Lindsey Buckingham,
arr. Geoff Lawson

156

162

166

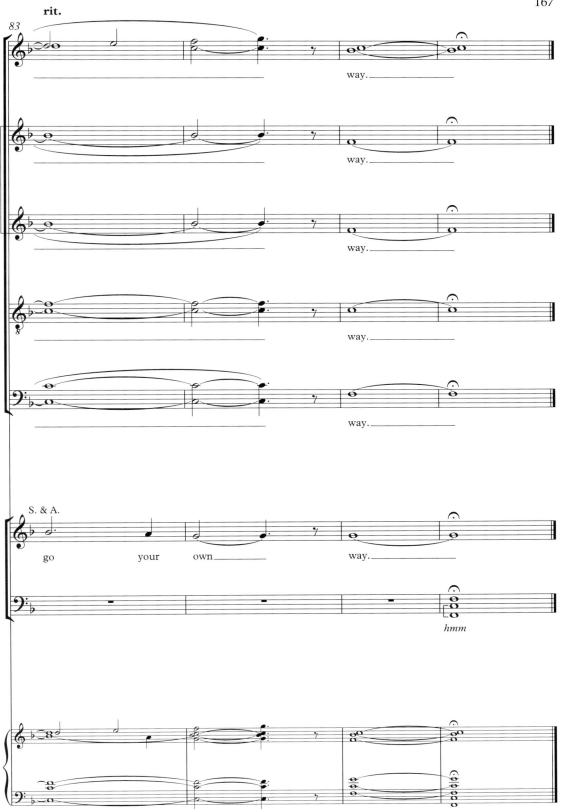

Passion Chorale

Music by Johann Sebastian Bach

123456789

MILITARY WIVES

The Military Wives are the inspirational choir formed by the wives and partners of British soldiers serving in Afghanistan. Created by Gareth Malone as part of the TV series *The Choir*, their moving performances in support of their loved ones on the frontline have touched the hearts of millions, and their debut single 'Wherever You Are', written for the choir by Paul Mealor, became the 2011 Christmas No.1.

With this book your choir can enjoy singing all of the tracks from the album, including 'In My Dreams', also composed by Paul Mealor, alongside beautiful versions of modern classics from artists such as Adele and Coldplay. Each song is presented in its original version for SSA choir, with piano accompaniment.

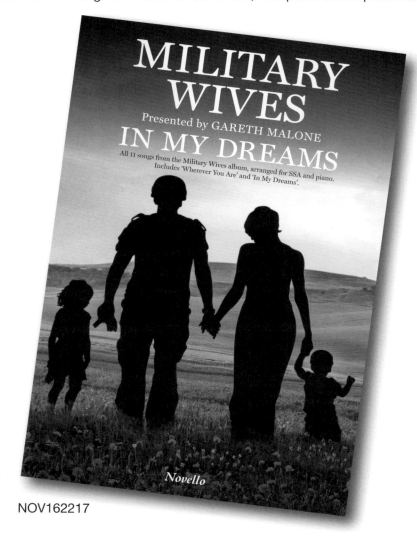

NOV162217

For more information on these and the thousands of other titles available from Music Sales, please contact:

Music Sales Limited
Newmarket Road, Bury St Edmunds, Suffolk, IP33 3YB.
www.musicsales.com

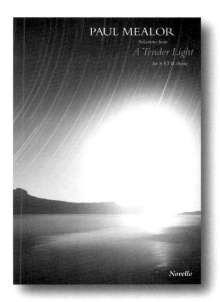

PAUL MEALOR

A Tender Light

for SATB chorus

NOV200926

Novello is proud to present selections from *A Tender Light*; a matching folio for Paul Mealor's latest choral album, including *Ubi Caritas* and *A Spotless Rose*.

A Tender Light is a collection of new choral music by the Welsh composer Paul Mealor, including *Ubi caritas*, made famous by its inclusion in the Royal Wedding Ceremony of His Royal Highness Prince William and Catherine Middleton (now TRH The Duke and Duchess of Cambridge) at Westminster Abbey in April 2011. 2.5 billion people (the largest audience in broadcasting history) heard his motet on that day and since then it has topped the classical singles charts in the USA, UK, Australia, France and New Zealand and has already entered the standard repertoire for many choirs. For singers wanting to explore further the music of Mealor, this book also contains the luminous *She Walks in Beauty*, the contemplative *O vos omnes* and the madrigal sequence *Now Sleeps the Crimson Petal*. *Locus iste* and *Ave Maria* are modern yet timeless settings of well-known texts. This is a must-have collection for any mixed-voice choir wanting to explore the latest and best in choral repertoire.

Now Sleeps The Crimson Petal
(Four Madrigals on Rose Texts)
Now sleeps the crimson petal
Lady, when I behold the roses sprouting
Upon a bank with roses
A Spotless Rose
She walks in beauty
O vos omnes
Locus Iste
Ave Maria
Ubi caritas

Born in St Asaph, North Wales in 1975, Paul Mealor studied composition as a boy with William Mathias, later with John Pickard at the University of York and in Copenhagen with Hans Abrahamsen and Per Nørgård. His music has been commissioned and performed at many festivals around the world by such ensembles as the BBC National Orchestra of Wales and the Britten Sinfonia, and has been broadcast on BBC Radio Two, Three, Four, Japanese, Swedish and Danish Radios and Classic FM. Mealor composes primarily for the voice and has written a number of cycles, songs and choral works for many leading singers and choirs in the UK and USA. Since January 2003 he has taught at the Music Department at the University of Aberdeen where he is Professor of Composition.

'This is music of deep introspection with luminous tonality and a real directness and openness of expression...
I wept tears of joy from beginning to end...'
NYE New York Magazine

'Serene and beautiful'
Gramophone

'Mealor is the most important composer to have emerged in Welsh choral music since William Mathias'
New York Times

Novello Publishing Limited
part of The Music Sales Group